Robin and the Rabbit
(A Book About Anxiety)

written by
Holly Duhig

Illustratred by
Drue Rintoul

BookLife
PUBLISHING

©2018
BookLife Publishing
King's Lynn
Norfolk PE30 4LS

All rights reserved.
Printed in Malaysia.

A catalogue record for this
book is available from the
British Library.

ISBN: 978-1-78637-359-5

Written by:
Holly Duhig

Edited by:
Madeline Tyler

Designed by:
Drue Rintoul

With grateful thanks to Place2Be for their endorsement of this series.

**These titles have been developed to support teachers and
school counsellors in exploring pupils' mental health, and have
been reviewed and approved by the clinical team at Place2Be,
the leading national children's mental health charity.**

When Robin wakes up to go to school, so does his rabbit. When Robin comes downstairs for breakfast, so does his rabbit. Rabbit is worried about the day ahead. He is telling Robin about all the things that could go horribly wrong.

Robin likes to start the day with a round of toast and jam.
Rabbit likes to start the day with a round of 'what ifs'.

"What if none of your friends want to play with you at break time?"
"What if you fail your spelling test?"

All of Rabbit's questions start to make Robin feel very unusual inside. His hands feel jittery, his stomach feels wishy-washy and his heart feels like it's playing jump rope inside his chest.

Rabbit doesn't think Robin should go to school today.

"What if you're sick in front of everyone?"

Robin hadn't thought of that, and it suddenly makes him feel much worse.

Robin's rabbit is like a bad doctor. He has lots of ideas about what could be wrong with Robin, but rabbits don't make very good doctors. They tend to hop to conclusions and they can't give out sick notes.

8

Robin asks his mum if he can stay at home today. She says Robin is probably just nervous about his spelling test. He doesn't know how to tell her that it feels much worse than that.

At school, the spelling test is about to begin. It isn't long before Rabbit hops up behind Robin and starts to twitch nervously. Rabbit always follows Robin to school, even when Robin tells him he doesn't need his help.

Rabbit is like a bad fortune teller. He tries to predict the future but he doesn't always get it right. He believes Robin is going to fail the spelling test. Robin finds it hard to ignore Rabbit's prediction.

Rabbit doesn't like tests. It feels like everyone's eyes are on him and Robin. All those eyes make him want to hide behind his ears or burrow under the desk.

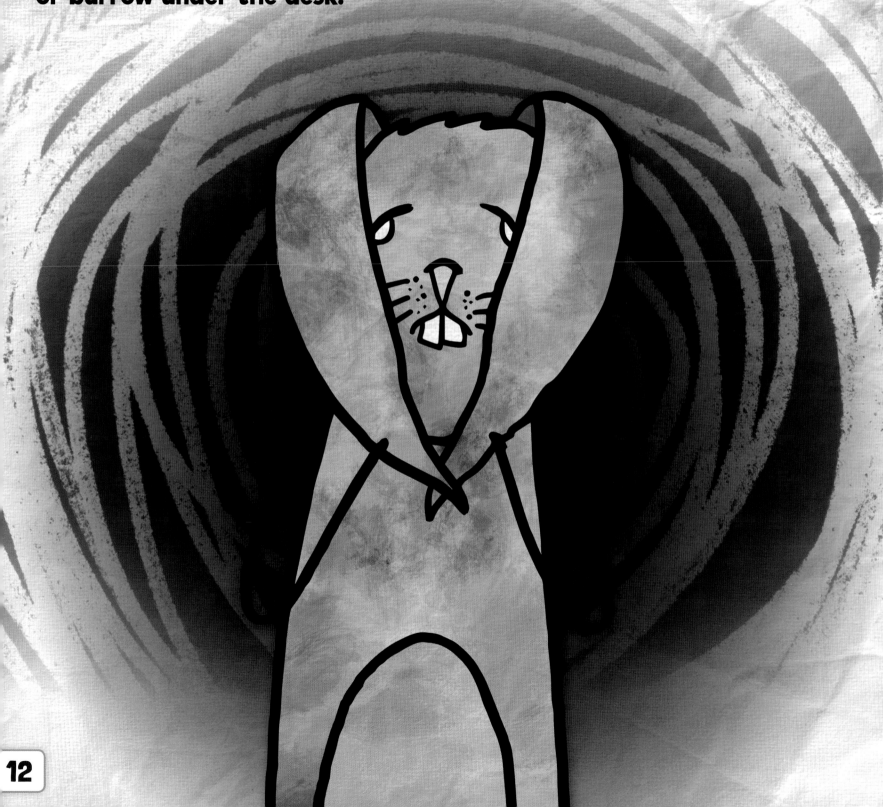

Robin tries to concentrate on his work, but Rabbit won't leave him alone! He has lots of 'what ifs' still to ask.

"What if you get the answers wrong?"

"What if your handwriting isn't neat enough?"

"What if all your friends do better than you?"

Rabbit won't stop rabbiting on and it's making the wishy-washy feeling in Robin's stomach come back. With every hop-skip-jump, Rabbit finds something new to worry about.

"What if you get sick in front of everyone?"

"What if you're too sick to pass the test?"

Rabbit wants Robin to run away. Rabbit is like a bad firefighter – he is always hitting the fire alarm even when there is no danger.

Robin's palms begin to sweat...

...his heart begins to race...

...he feels dizzy and out of breath.

Robin makes a bolt for the door and Rabbit runs behind him.
He's running really fast. He runs and he runs and he runs...

OOOFF!

...straight into Mr Wainwright.

Robin's cheeks turn as red as a fire engine when he realises what he has done. Rabbit cowers behind him.

"What on Earth is the matter, Robin?" asks Mr Wainwright in his soft, rumbling voice.

When Robin sees that Mr Wainwright isn't cross, he tells him all about his troublesome rabbit and all the 'what ifs' and, to his surprise, Mr Wainwright listens patiently.

"Sounds like you're in need of a rabbit trainer, Robin," he says. "Luckily, I know just the person..."

Mr Wainwright takes Robin to see the school counsellor. Her name is Gemma, and she says it's her job to train troublesome rabbits.

She tells him that rabbits are very anxious creatures and that's why they make bad doctors and bad fortune tellers and even bad firefighters!

Gemma tells Robin that everybody needs a rabbit from time-to-time.

"If Rabbit turns up when you are crossing a busy road, he will remind you to stay safe. In fact, Rabbits make excellent lifeguards!"

Robin thinks about it. Rabbit could come to the rescue if he's ever in danger and leave him alone when he's not. Gemma teaches Robin when it's okay to listen to Rabbit and when it's okay to tell him to hop off!

Gemma asks Robin to think about Rabbit's 'what ifs' really hard. What would really happen if Robin failed his spelling test? Mr Wainwright would probably let him have another go, or he would get a bad mark but do better next time.

Maybe the things that Rabbit thinks are emergencies aren't really that scary after all.

Rabbit likes his new role as a lifeguard, and Robin likes the peace and quiet! And, if Rabbit ever becomes too much to handle again, he knows where to find a first-class rabbit trainer who can help Robin put him in his place.

More Information

Everyone feels anxious from time-to-time but, when someone feels anxious a lot of the time, and it stops them from being happy in their daily life, they might have an anxiety disorder. An anxiety disorder is a mental health condition which means it affects your mind. Anxiety can make you feel tired, unwell and cause you to miss out on the things you enjoy doing; it can also make it difficult to concentrate.

Anxiety can be difficult to cope with, but it can be managed. If you are feeling anxious and are struggling to cope, talking to someone you trust – like a doctor, counsellor, parent or carer – is the first step to getting help.